THE
EMBODIED
WRITING
JOURNAL

CLAIMING YOUR BODY STORY
FOR HEALING
AND WHOLENESS

By Ellie Roscher

The art of embodiment is not new, nor owned by any individual. I honor and acknowledge the teachers before me who sought ways to connect our hearts, minds, and bodies. I am informed by the ancient wisdom of several lineages including Christian monasticism, the eight-limbed path of Ashtanga yoga with roots in Ancient India, and yin yoga, which incorporates principles of Chinese Taoist philosophy.

I am grateful for my writing teachers, most notably Jo Ann Beard, Verlyn Klinkenborg, Enuma Okoro, Chanequa Walker-Barnes, and Jonathan Wilson-Hartgrove, who have taught me so much through their presence, craft, classes, and books. A few of the prompts in this journal were inspired by my time learning from them as well as from the recommended resources you will find at the end.

"Revolution begins with the self, in the self."

—TONI CADE-BAMBARA,
The Black Woman: An Anthology

Introduction

There is a deep wisdom in our very flesh, if we can only come to
our senses and feel it.

—ELIZABETH A. BEHNKE,
quoted in *My Grandmother's Hands*

In this life, I want to inhabit my body. For me, yoga, running, and medita-
tion are three paths toward deeper embodiment. So is writing. Reflective
writing has been proven to have positive effects for our health. It creates
a sense of space in our bodies and thoughts so that, rather than react, we
can respond in our daily lives. In writing we can turn up the volume on the
quiet voice inside us telling the truth. We get to live our lives a second time,
walking through our memories with curiosity and reverence. Writing can
hone our noticing muscle and help us get unstuck. We put our thoughts and
stories on the page, creating a geographical distance between the words and
our bodies. We can look at the raw material, notice, contend with it, and
work with it, molding it like clay. We become the author, the narrator, the
main character, and the audience member in the front-row seat.

Our bodies have a story. Tending to the stories of our bodies can help
us honor our bodies, and usher in and grow self-compassion and wisdom.
It encourages continued vulnerability, unfolding, and expanding. When
we break, we can break open. We can seek not perfection, but wholeness.
There is no arriving. We can revise our body stories with new information
and insight, applying meaning where we did not see it before. A blank page
is a great listener.

For years now, I have invited my writing, theology, and yoga students
tell the stories of their bodies. I encourage fellow peacemakers to make
peace in their own bodies, to start the revolution in their beings. It is rigor-
ous, vulnerable, and profound work. It is simple but not easy. It is one tool of
many available to walk the embodied path. Weaving the story of our bodies
into our being helps us integrate more fully, inhabit our bodies, and live an
embodied life.

You can use this journal on its own or in conjunction with my book, *The
Embodied Path*. Writing prompts in this journal fall into two major catego-

ries. Some are emotional writing prompts, which help us process through stuck-ness in our feeling bodies to live into flow. Others are prompts will aid you in creating and claiming your body story. There is a myriad of benefits to reflective, embodied writing, of which I will focus on four:

First, crafting our body stories forges meaning and expands identity.

Many things happen to us that do not make sense. We get sick, we get assaulted, we live with depression. Telling a story about these things will not help them make sense. Some suffering we endure will never make sense. Yet, with time, we can choose to look back at our lives and craft stories that make meaning. The way we make meaning will influence who we are and who we become. Not all moments carry equal meaning. We mine our memories and find the ones that hold weight and carry a charge. We make a meaningful story by choosing those moments, putting them in some order, raising themes, and assigning importance. We shift our role to narrator. Observing our memories and crafting a story from them is empowering. The stories we tell reveal why we think our lives are worth living, adding dignity and hope. Claiming coherence in the chaos, folding the hard moments into a narrative, brings worth as we transcend the superficial and momentary. Our lives take on a significance bigger than ourselves. Forging meaning can give you the vocabulary you need to fight for your freedom, dropping the constraints the world puts on us. Andrew Solomon says it this way: "There is always someone who wants to confiscate our humanity. And there are always stories that restore it."

Second, crafting our body stories carves space to process trauma.

Your body has an amazing ability to protect you and survive. In *My Grandmother's Hands,* Resmaa Menakem reminds us that our bodies hold the trauma from our lives and unhealed dissonance and trauma of our ancestors. Trauma as a defensive maneuver, a protective response to an event that it perceives as dangerous, that was too much, too often, too fast, and you experience the world as unsafe. Your system got overwhelmed. Healing is hard, but so is not healing, and healing from trauma cannot be rushed. If you are working through body trauma, do it with trained professionals. The work of this journal, being tied to words, should happen in a time and place where you feel safe and calm and when you are ready to attach words to memories. Carving out time to tell your body story can create space enough to process and slowly move through pain toward healing and wholeness one layer at a time. As bell hooks writes, "The longing to tell one's story and the process of telling is symbolically a gesture of longing to recover the past in such a way that one experiences both a sense of reunion and a sense of release."

Third, crafting our body stories works to dismantle the hierarchical separation between the mind and the body.

Plato and the Stoics were skeptical of the body. Stoics valued lack of passion as the highest virtue. The mind's job was to control the body and suppress emotion. Plato said sacred love was that of the immortal soul and profane love was that of the body. Mind–body dualism considers the body dirty and mortal, something to be denied and transcended. The highest place in society was held by the elite males, politicians, and philosophers who could live and work in the mind. Women and laborers were inferior, living and working in the body. This dualism remains alive today in our mind-over-matter mentality. Yet mind–body dualism is simply not working. Our bodies are wise, and we can only override their signals for so long. We cannot think our way out of a feeling problem. Ignoring our bodies delays healing.

Engaging in this work, you may experience real barriers, especially if you identify as White, male, heterosexual, able, Western, or Christian, in part because of the stronghold of mind–body dualism. Be patient with yourself. Some of the barriers may be very old. Honor your ancestors and engage in the work of subversive embodied storytelling.

Fourth, crafting our body narratives as counter-stories can shift dismissive and limiting master narratives.

Society's master narratives treat individuals like a group. They tell us who we are and who we are not, setting standards that require conformity and assimilation. Our master narratives are used to justify oppression and maintain the status quo. For example, master narratives in our society would have me believe that, as a woman, I am inferior to a man, that my value depreciates as I age, and that I'm too fragile to contend with my own internalized misogyny. I have learned helplessness to unlearn, and creating a counter-story can help. Counter-stories resist, repudiate, subvert, contest, and undermine the master narrative. The narrative acts of insubordination set out to shift the oppressive master narrative and, in so doing, can create more freedom and agency in the storyteller. It can also shift the perspective of the dominant group if taken up. Counter-stories create opportunities for narrative resistance and repair. In our disembodied culture, body stories are inherently counter stories. Here, you can create your own counter-story, which can help individuals, institutions, and society be less cruel. Hearing and understanding each other's stories will accompany us toward personal and communal peace.

A certain kind of guided, detailed writing can not only help us process what we've been through and assist us as we envision a path forward; it can lower our blood pressure, strengthen our immune system, and increase our general well-being. Expressive writing can result in a reduction in stress, anxiety, and depression; improve our sleep and performance; and bring us greater focus and clarity.

DEBORAH SIEGEL-ACEVEDO

Be gentle with yourself.

What does being gentle with yourself mean right now?

_____

_____

_____

_____

_____

_____

_____

_____

_____

_____

_____

_____

Name one way you can extend kindness to your body right now.

_____

_____

_____

_____

_____

_____

_____

_____

_____

_____

_____

Tap into your courage.

What's scary or uncertain about emotional
writing and crafting your body story?

Describe what it means to be brave instead of perfect.

A few things to consider

*   Your story doesn't have to be grammatically perfect or creatively crafted. Let the story be as beautiful, messy, and unedited as real life.

*   Try writing in the present tense to access the richness of memories and hold them close.

*   If it helps, set a timer for each writing prompt—maybe for seven to ten minutes—and write without overthinking for the time allotted.

*   Don't worry if your story is not linear or redemptive. Bring in a sense of culture, place, and community.

*   To hear the quiet inner voice speaking its truth, silence and stillness help.

*   Claim the role of author in your life. Do writing that is just for you. Distinguish between private and personal. You don't need to go somewhere you are not ready to go, and you don't have to share your story unless you are ready.

*   Did you ever get growing pains in your shins when you were a kid? I remember that aching so well. Growing hurts. You are outgrowing your former boundaries, your restrictive stories. You cannot be contained.

So let us pick up the stones over which we stumble, friends, and build altars. Let us listen to the sound of breath in our bodies. Let us listen to the sounds of our own voices, of our own names, of our own fears. Let us name the harsh light and soft darkness that surround us. Let's claw ourselves out from the graves we've dug. Let's lick the earth from our fingers. Let us look up and out and around. The world is big and wide and wild and wonderful and wicked, and our lives are murky, magnificent, malleable, and full of meaning. Oremus. Let us pray.

—PÁDRAIG Ó TUAMA,
DAILY PRAYER WITH THE CORRYMEELA COMMUNITY

Bodies Break:
Living With Limitation

"To be 'well' is not to live in a state of perpetual safety and calm, but to move fluidly from a state of adversity, risk, adventure, or excitement, back to safety and calm, and out again. Stress is not bad for you; being stuck is bad for you. Wellness happens when your body is a place of safety for you, even when your body is not necessarily in a safe place. You can be well, even during the times when you don't feel good."

—EMILY AND AMELIA NAGOSKI,
Burnout: The Secret to Unlocking the Stress Cycle

While pregnant with my first child, I experienced a body fatigue I had never known before. I was nauseated all day, curled in on myself. While awake, I longed to be sleeping. While upright, I dreamed of being horizontal. I dragged myself through the day. Then I got shingles, and I gave up trying. Rest was nonnegotiable. I spent hours on the couch not really watching The Good Wife or The West Wing, chosen in part because of the sheer number of episodes. I had never moved so little for so long. I felt depressed and isolated on the sidelines, like I was waiting to live my life again. Like those hours, days, weeks, and months didn't count. Like I didn't matter. It felt like when I was a young athlete sitting out of practices and competitions while my injuries healed, watching my teammates, pining. Or right after COVID-19 stay-at-home orders, when I quit my job to facilitate online learning for my children. I grieved the loss of my public life and the value placed on contributing. Our society is structured around the productivity of the strong. Our master narratives would have us believe that weakness should be overcome and avoided at all costs. The master narratives of the dominant culture value young, healthy, able bodies. They encourage us to deny our mortality and strive for unattainable perfection. Bodies that are marked by physical, emotional, or mental limitations are discarded and isolated in little and not-so-little ways.

In other times and places, people believed illness was a divine judgment and punishment, so people who were sick deserved it. Lepers were quarantined in colonies. Folks living with mental illness were sent away to asylums where they were not seen or heard. Societies were built around efficiency and speed, and those who did not belong were removed. Residue from this broken and fearful logic remains. People living with illnesses such as lung cancer, HIV/AIDS and diabetes, and mental health issues like depression and anxiety are blamed and judged. Society creates distance as if we could catch these ailments like a cold.

The COVID-19 outbreak gave and continues to give us an opportunity to contend with our flawed assumptions around body limitations, contagiousness, and worth. We are all on the dynamic, ever-shifting continuum of ableness, illness, and wellness. We all take on dis-ease and claim strength where we can. Looking back on the moments I felt sidelined, I can see my value. The *stories* were defective, not me. Exploring themes of wellness and ability in our bodies can shift our societal structures so that all bodies have value and are accommodated fully into mainstream society. Nature needs diversity to thrive.

The prompts in this section explore the themes of sickness, wellness, and ableness. They create agency in you as narrator while putting pressure on the narratives that value speed, production, and survival of the fittest. We experience suffering when our bodies present limits. It's a reminder of our ultimate mortality. Individually and collectively, we will benefit from slowing down, listening, and learning from our amazing and imperfect bodies. There is strength in gentleness and wisdom in the vulnerability of human limitation.

Spend 30 seconds on each of the quadrants listing things
you have noticed and experienced in your day pertaining to
the different senses. This exercise warms up your brain to
write and helps awaken your senses so you can live in your
body more often and notice what you are noticing.

Touched	**Heard**
Saw	**Smelled**

What activity do you rush through? What is one thing
you can do to listen to your body today?

Take a moment to offer your body gratitude for what it can do.
What is an activity you enjoy that encourages slow, deep listening?

Who in your community gets isolated or sent away? What is one
thing you can do to see them and advocate for a system change?

What is the coolest thing your body can do?

What is something you really enjoy doing while your body is active?
While your body is still?

What is something you live with and will live with long term
that has no cure? What is something "chronic" that you carry
with you and manage? What are the tools you use?

What is something we would know about you by looking at your
body? What is something about you that we cannot see?

Which bodies in society are you taught not
to see? Who gets sent away?

Write about a time you literally or figuratively
fell and decided to get back up again.

Take the witness view of a time you were sick and offer yourself some tender affection. Write about it. What is one thing you can do to relationally traverse the demarcation between the sick and the well?

Write about a time when you were sidelined from society.

When you have experienced brokenness, how does the urge
to bounce back, rush healing, and get back to normal
show up for you? What opportunity does the brokenness
present to learn, grow, and unfold into wholeness?

Write about how your physical health and
mental health relate to each other.

Write about a time that one limitation led to an increased capacity in another way.

What has your body lost? What has been taken away?

How do you feel your worth tied to productivity?

What are the master narratives in your birth family, found family, place of work, media, and society at large around limitations: physical and mental illness, injury, aging, and death? Are body limits talked about, integrated, or ignored? Are bodies viewed as lacking or is focus placed on our systems? Do you have any counter-stories that could alter the perception of the dominant culture?

How do we as individuals and our community benefit from telling and listening to more stories that challenge myths of independence, wellness, and ability? How might our narratives become healthier and more interesting? How might your identity shift? Who might benefit from an increased sense of agency and freedom?

The stories we are born into are important, influential, and powerful.
Draw your family tree as far back as you can. Identify the storytellers
in your family and ask them to tell you stories. Listen hard. Where
did you come from? What stories from your ancestors shaped you?
What stories that get told about you do you reject? Claim?

Write about a time when you came face to face with the
limitations of your human body, maybe through illness or injury.
What part of your ability or health were you taking for granted?
We are dependent on so many things and people to survive. We
break. We are mortal. And we heal and adapt. We are resilient.
We survive. What is your story of living with limitation?

Bodies Connect:
Expanding the Love

"We will not end white-body supremacy—or any other form of human evil—by trying to tear it to pieces. Instead, we can offer people better ways to belong and better things to belong to. Each of us can also build our own capacity for genuine belonging."

—RESMAA MENAKEM,
My Grandmother's Hands

At a recent yoga training, the facilitator had us sit facing another person, our knees almost touching, and our eyes closed. The practice would be to hold each other's eye contact in silence for several minutes. When the facilitator invited us to open our eyes, I instinctually leaned forward without realizing it. She cued us to stack our shoulders over our hips, and I leaned back. In that moment, I felt a deeper alignment in my body that opened a sense of expansion in my being. I had more room to hold my partner's gaze. I had more space to offer her. It felt like I could have stayed in that posture of connection, holding expansive space for love, forever.

I think about this moment a lot. My tendency is to pitch forward, literally and figuratively. I jump ahead to the future. I hold my mind in higher esteem than my body. I lead with my ego and my intellect. I lean forward to guard my chest, protect my heart, and hide my abdomen. I lean forward because I want you to know I am here, I am with you, I've got you. I lean forward to ingratiate myself to you and put your needs first. I lean forward because I do not want you to think by pulling back that I am pulling away.

In the yoga exercise, when I did pull back, I was not pulling away. I was pulling myself into alignment so I could exist from my core. It brought ease and expansion. In wanting to connect with my partner, I was hindering the quality of my ability to connect. My tendency is to pitch forward. My mindful work is to pull not away but back into alignment so I can connect more deeply and authentically.

We were born social, designed to be in relationship. Babies need to be held to survive. We crave closeness, intimacy, and a true sense of belonging. We do not walk the embodied path in a vacuum by ourselves. Although the work can benefit from quiet time alone to feel, write, and process, the work is not solitary. We want to belong to our own bodies, and we want to belong to each other. We want to belong to beautiful and body-affirming community.

The writing prompts in this section explore how our bodies are astounding tools of connection. Not by escaping our bodies, but rather more fully entering our bodies, we can live from our core in a way that makes real, deep, and true connection with others possible.

Set a timer for five minutes and without pausing or overthinking it,
fill the time completing this sentence:
"What I meant to say is..."

Which of your senses do you under-utilize?
What is something you can do to re-engage that sense?

Do you use your body to speak?
Do you choose your words carefully?
What is your body language communicating right now?

What is your body doing when you feel a deep connection
to a person or to an activity?

Who is a person you looked up when you were young,
who was walking a path you were interested in?
What is one way you can support representation in society?

Has your community ever asked you to hide a part of who you are?

What groups have you worked to change from the inside? Where is one place you can put your body on purpose to advocate for human rights?

With whom in your life would you like to build a deeper connection?

Write about a moment when music communicated something to you.

Write about a moment something was happening to your
body that you did not want to be happening. How has your
identity expanded in response to that moment?

Write about a time your words were misunderstood or when words fell short. How can you better use your tools beyond your words to communicate?

Are there two parts of your identity that are in
conflict? How do you work toward wholeness?

What do you need but are afraid to ask for?

When in your life has your body served
another person or the community?

How does your body connect with other bodies on social media? How do tools of technology enhance connection? How is it limiting?

Write about a time you use felt deep connection to others.
Where did that sense of connection show up in your body?

Create a list of five objects from your past. Then choose one that and write more deeply about the memories that are living in that object.

Write about a time when you were able to connect and
communicate beautifully without using words.

Write a letter to someone with whom you desire deeper connection. Say the things that need to be said.

Deepen your connection to yourself. Your 80-year-old self meets...

...your 20-year-old self

...you right now

...you in 5 years

What does the 80-year-old say to all the versions
of you? (Feel free to pick different ages.)

Bodies Persevere:
Choosing Our Story

"The wound is the place where the Light enters you."

—RUMI,
Suffering and Hope in the Enchanting Garb of Poetry

When I work with teenagers, I have them brainstorm and categorize the myriad messages they receive from the outside world, asking, "What words would your parents or guardians use to describe you? How about your siblings and extended family? How might your teachers describe you? Or your coaches? What words would your friends use? What role do you play in your friend group? Who would your teammates say that you are? Your classmates? How might a stranger looking at your social media profiles describe you?"

I have them look at the list and notice who sees them clearly, who may have a limited or misguided view, and which messages if any might be untrue and downright harmful. They notice which messages resonate. They make intentional choices as to which messages to accept, which to revise, and which to dismiss. I ask them, "Who do you say that you are?" They write a series of "I am" statements that reflect their true self.

The messages we receive from other people can be powerful when we internalize them, influencing us to live small. We can get used to and get comfortable in the boxes others make for us even if they are restricting. Minnie Bruce Pratt writes that every time our limited being expands, we experience it as an "upheaval, not catastrophe, more like a snake shedding its skin than like death. The old constriction is sloughed off with difficulty, but there is an expansion: not a change in basic shape, but an expansion, some growth, some reward for struggle and curiosity." The change, the growth, and the expansion can feel like a loss. We are letting go of lies and habitual ways of living that were familiar and comfortable. Even if they were limited, they were ours. Pratt wonders, "Our fear of the losses can keep us from changing. What is it, exactly, we are afraid to lose?"

This section prompts body stories about recognizing how other people's stories about you might not be serving you. Be brave enough to deny the constricting messages from other people and write your own expansive stories. Slough off the old skin, sustain the loss, and embrace the growing pains. In so doing, grow your sense of freedom and agency in your body. Became more embodied, more in touch with your true self and live toward deeper healing and wholeness.

Set a timer for five minutes and for that time write messages you have received about who you are and who you should be from other people and society. They may come as sound bites or more subtle messages. Cross out all the messages that you do not want to take on.

Set a timer for five minutes and fill the time writing "I am" statements. Who do you say that you are?

What is one thing you can do that you enjoy, that
brings you pleasure, that helps you live embodied?

What is a character trait you have inherited? From whom?

Where do you sense restriction, resistance, or fear in
your body? Who or what supports your opening?

Who are you trying to please? How?

What is your body doing when you feel powerful?

What does your hair say about you?

Has there ever been an activity that helped
heal a relationship in your life?

What messages did you receive about your body as a child?

How were you pegged in school?

When was a time you did something to please
someone else at the expense of yourself?

What are you running away from? What are you running toward?

How are you pegged now at work, in your family, in the world?

Who and what has helped you remember who you are and place your attention on the traits you want to grow?

What narratives have other people told about you that you have had to let go of to live into who you really are? Talk about a time when other people wanted you to be someone you did not want to be.

Which words are you sick of repressing? What do you still need to say?

What are you an expert in? Where does your intelligence shine?

How might your body story shift and expand the master
narratives that pressure you to conform?

Pick a body part and write three snapshots of that body part from three different seasons of your life. Repeat the prompt later with other body parts or other snapshots.

Write the story of a time you lived through adversity. How did it affect your body? Your thoughts? Your identity? Did your identity shift by surviving the hardship? How do you choose to apply meaning now looking back? Take some time to honor the resilience in your body and being.

Bodies Transform:
Embracing our Ever-Unfolding Identity

"Once you start approaching your body with curiosity rather than fear, everything shifts."

—BESSEL VAN DER KOLK,
The Body Keeps the Score

At my child's six-year-old checkup, he weighed in at around fifty pounds. I gained and lost that much weight with each full-term pregnancy. I looked at his long, growing body and imagined carrying him around all day and sleeping with him attached to my body all night without a break. And I marveled at my own strength. I pause on my sporadic gray hairs, my cesarean section scar, my smile lines, my crooked pinky toe, and the scar on the roof of my mouth, all laced with stories. My tight jaw, an emerging bunion, and rounded shoulders are all signs of my daily patterns and posturing in the world. Layers of stress pile up over time, and it takes time, then, to unravel and unlearn too.

My affection toward my body shifts as my understanding of what it has been through and what it is capable of expands. I become. As I age, I care more about what I think about my body than what the world thinks. I am the best person to care for me. My edges soften with growing reverence, compassion, and respect for my body and its story.

Can you remember inhabiting your child body? Do you remember what it looked like and felt like, not from pictures but from your own vantage point? Our bodies change over time, as do our stories about our bodies, and with those transformations our identities shift. Our bodies have been through so much over time, and it shows in how we transform.

The prompts in this section are centered around body transformation. It is an invitation to forge meaning and expand identity as you tell the story of your body. Honor how your body is changing in joyful, painful, complicated, and incredible ways. You are a living example of the fluidity of bodies and identity. Bravely and counter-culturally become, accepting change as an opportunity to not stay small or bounce back or hide but to expand in unexpected and powerful ways.

Lies I tell myself, other people have told me, or those society tells me about my body.	The Truth

Fill in the T chart. Recognize which lie or lies on the left side carry the most weight or have the most charge to them. This may be one of your core lies. Spend some time here. What experiences contributed to creating that lie? Choose the phrase on the right side of that core lie and take it on as a daily mantra, a refrain you can repeat to yourself throughout the day.

Set a timer for seven minutes. Write a litany of sentences that all start with the phrase "I remember..." Don't overthink it. Don't stop writing. Just see what comes up without trying to control it. You will end up with a list of memories that will not be chronological but do correlate. When the time goes off, stop writing. Take a look at your list. Choose a memory that carries a lot of charge for you and go back to that memory. Walk around in the memory, noticing. Journal about what comes up and notice how the memory feels in your body.

I remember...

Is there a part of your body that makes you feel different, or marked, that you are ashamed of? Will telling the story of that body part soften something for you?

What is something your body can do that may be gendered by society but feels like your own superpower?

What is one choice you can make to express your gender in a way that feels in line with the person you really are?

Do you more often escape your body by dwelling in your mind or escape your mind by dwelling in your body?

Have you ever been ashamed of a part of your body because you felt it was different from the norm?

What are some ways you like receiving physical
affection? Giving physical affection?

What is one thing you can do today to celebrate a
part of who you are that rarely gets prioritized?

How did you express gender as a small child?

What messages did you receive through puberty about
your gender that you have internalized?

When was a time you did not feel at home in your body?

What version of yourself may benefit from some tender compassion?

How does your sense of self transform as your context changes?

How does your body experience connection
to others across time and space?

Write about a time in your life when your body went through a major transition or transformation. How did your identity shift? Did your sense of freedom and agency grow, shrink, or stay the same?

What do master narratives tell around major body transformations
like pregnancy, gender confirmation, or reconstructive
surgery? Do the narratives that exist in your birth family,
found family, place of work, communities, and society at
large allow space for major body transformations?

Where are you when you take your body for granted? Where are you when you are very aware of your body and how it is being perceived?

How might you befriend yourself more deeply?

Write a memory from travel and what you learned
about yourself outside your more regular context.

Write about how your body and your relationship
to your body has shifted over time.

Bodies Overcome:
Surviving Oppressive Systems

"Counterstories take up an oppressive but shared moral understanding and attempt to shift it, rejecting its assumption that
people with a particular group identity are to be subordinated
to others or denied access to personal and social goods. They
are, then, narrative acts of insubordination."

—HILDE LINDEMANN NELSON,
Damaged Identities: Narrative Repair

In high school I absent-mindedly scheduled a meeting in a room that a
group member couldn't get to in his wheelchair. When I got married, I
invited friends to attend who could not yet legally marry due to their sexuality. A few months after George Floyd was murdered in my town, I got
pulled over for speeding with my kids in the car. A White-bodied female
officer gave me a ticket and sent me on my way. I was aware that I was not
afraid. In December, I am attuned to my Christian identity watching our
media culture center Christmas. Chanequa Walker-Barnes writes, "In any
society, the most marginalized people best understand the rules of the system, because they need to know the politics and dynamics in order to avoid
being crushed by them."

Apart from being a woman, my body is supported by the structures
of my country. As someone not being crushed by the system, I can locate
and implicate myself in the systems that do crush others. I can see where I
have long-held privilege in my body without being paralyzed and broken by
shame. I can see the action and attitudes of individuals and see the patterns,
policies, cultures, and systems advantaging certain bodies, often bodies like
mine, over others. I can move past passive empathy to action. It is the work
of feeling in my body and knowing in my bones that systemic oppression
constricts the psyche of the oppressed and wounds the soul of the oppres-
sor. It is the work of unlearning innocence and learned helplessness.

The master narratives favor my body over others and lead to attitudes,
policies, and practices that dismiss, limit, and attempt to erase some bodies more than others. The prompts in this section address the fatigue and

vigilance it takes to stay safe in a body marked as other and less than by the dominant culture. We can write as narrative acts of insubordination, actively countering the limiting narratives coming at us from the systems level. As bell hooks writes, "My writing was an act of resistance not simply in relation to outer structures of domination like race, sex, and class; I was writing to resist all the socialization I had received in a religious, southern, working-class, patriarchal home that tried to teach me silence as the most desirable trait of womanliness." Our stories speak into the silence. They can assert truth that is always already there, truth remembered. And they can work to shift our master narratives so we can all deconstruct oppressive systems together and build communities where all bodies can be safe and belong.

Set a timer for seven minutes. Rip this page from the journal. Start the timer and write about whatever is disturbing your peace. Don't pick your pen up, don't edit as you go, don't worry about sentences or grammar. When the timer goes off, don't reread it. Destroy the paper by tearing it up or safely setting it on fire. Don't direct the energy that came out of your body toward yourself. Your goal is to get feelings of dis-ease out of your body and let them go so you can access your body story with more neutralized energy.

What identity groups do you belong to?

What is your favorite thing about being a woman/
man/ non-binary person? What is hard about it?

Call to mind a piece of clothing or jewelry that
is saturated with memories. How does it express
alignment between the inner and outer you?

If you could break one gender rule without any social consequences, which one would you choose?

Has your body ever been the center of attention in a room of people? Did you feel safe?

Have you ever been labeled by someone else because of a choice you made about self-expression? Did that label feel accurate? Did it limit or expand your sense of identity?

What policies place some bodies in the center and some bodies on the margins? What is one thing you can do to help change that policy?

Write about a time when you realized you were (insert your race, social class, citizenship status, or religion here).

Write about a time when you realized you were (insert your gender, sex, or sexuality here).

What binaries do you get put in? (man/woman, heterosexual/
homosexual, Black/White, etc.) In what ways are you
divided in half? Tugged at from two sides?

How have you felt pressure to behave, quiet down, or tone down your self-expression? How can you push back against that pressure in life-giving ways that support creativity and your true unfolding self?

Think about the choices you make and the ways you outwardly express your identity. Do you think about social consequences, or do you factor in your physical safety when making these choices?

How can you be a part of dismantling that system that divides us by race? How can you help build something new?

How has your gender identity and expression shifted over time?

Who are you with, what are you doing, and where are you when you feel like you belong? In what ways do you feel a sense of dis-belonging?

Write about a time you were very aware of your race, gender, or religious affiliation (or lack thereof). Then write about a time your body was at ease in your context.

How do master narratives perpetuate racism,
sexism, heterosexism, and xenophobia?

Write a story about your body navigating society's systems.
How can your body story expand your freedom and agency
while putting pressure on master narratives to expand?

Moving beyond passive empathy, what are you sensing is your body work to move toward more healing and wholeness at the systems level?

Bodies Remember:
Welcoming Ourselves Back Home

"Home is not where you are born; home is where all your attempts to escape cease."

—NAGUIB MAHFOUZ
Quoted in Transnational Identity and Memory Making
in the Lives of Iraqi Women in Diaspora

While teaching together at the same high school, one of the most beautiful women I know said to me, "I'm so glad I was not a pretty teenager." When I challenged her a bit she said, "I was not stereotypically pretty or ugly. I didn't stand out. Watching some of these pretty girls navigate the male gaze and the attention they get for their looks, now, looking back, I'm just lucky I didn't have to deal with that."

I was not stereotypically pretty in high school either. I never got made fun of for my looks, and I didn't get much positive attention for my looks either. I did not keep up on fashion, fads, or primping rituals. I didn't have great hair. My strong, athletic body kept me outside the slender feminine ideal. I didn't date much. I loved school and sports and enjoyed my friends. And as an adult, I also feel lucky.

I was aware of the male gaze, but rarely paralyzed by or beholden to it.

Our master narratives around who and what is pretty are relentlessly cruel. The standard is impossibly high and ever-changing, driving our consumer society forward. Weight loss, fast fashion, exercise, and cosmetic companies use social media to make people feel worthless and believe that the next product will make them pretty and desirable to others, which will in turn make them enough. Other people tell you if you are pretty or not. You don't have much control, and you must keep changing to please different standards of what is pretty.

Let's counter the dismissive master narratives around pretty. Let's live into our own beauty. Let's put down the drive for pretty and finally see that we are, indeed, full of beauty. Our bodies are beautiful. They are. And if you don't feel beautiful, it may be in part because the world's loud master narratives have a tiny, boring, and limiting standard of pretty. Our work is to tell the story from the inside out. To seek beauty inside us and all around us—listen to beautiful music, seek out beautiful art, eat beautiful food, sit in beautiful nature—so we ingest beauty and exude beauty and thus make the world more beautiful with our easy presence. Beautiful people glow. They naturally remind other people of their beauty. They live out of their bodies as home.

This is part of the work of our lives—to put down the rigged game of striving for pretty from a place of not-enough-ness and fiercely commit to the slow process of turning inward, honoring our true selves, and filling up. Beauty in. Beauty out. We are not the subject of another's gaze. We are the one sitting in the front row seat in a gorgeous world with beauty all around us. We are the beautiful main character of our own wild story. We take in beauty. We are beauty. We grow it and offer it around. When we put down pretty, we can continually welcome ourselves back home to our beautiful bodies.

Regardless of where you were born, where are you from? Finish the phrase "I am from..." with ordinary items, product names, home descriptions, plant names, family traditions, family traits, name of family members, description of family tendencies, something you were told as a child, representative of religion or lack thereof, place of birth or family far away, description of home, country or culture, and food items.

1.

2.

3.

4.

5.

6.

7.

8.

9.

10.

11.

12.

13.

14.

15.

Write a list of things that bring you pleasure. Think about food, drinks, music, relationships, objects, and activities. How can you prioritize these things?

What is one thing you can do to be kind to and affectionate with your body?

Take a few moments to watch a baby or small child move and be in their body. Can children encourage you to turn toward your body with renewed wonder at its beauty?

Have you felt your desirability wane with age? What is one thing you can do today to honor the beauty that emerges over time?

Have you ever adjusted your wardrobe to hide parts of your body?

Are there people, things, ideas, or activities that help
you align your sense of inner and outer beauty?

How do you (or don't you) live up to the impossible beauty standards
of society? Does that affect your self-talk or your actions? Can
you name the standards as the problem, not your body?

What messages did you receive about your body as a child?

How did your family, friends, and people you dated affect
your feelings and beliefs about what is pretty?

Write about a person in your life you consider beautiful.
What traits in that person do you admire?

How do you see the difference between pretty and beautiful? What holds you back from feeling beautiful?

What are the major barriers to you experiencing your body as home? What supports you experiencing your body as home?

In your mind and aloud, how do you talk to your body?
How do you talk about the bodies of other people?

Write a letter of resignation for a role, task, or long-held belief that is no longer serving you.

Take on the voice of LOVE. What does LOVE have
to say to you about your beauty?

Has your sense of your own beauty shifted over the years?

If the scars on your body could speak, what stories would they tell?

Find a picture of yourself as a child that conjures up some affection in you. Pick a photo at a specific age when you were dependent or vulnerable. Focus on the image in detail, allowing memories to surface. Practice tender compassion on your child self. Write a letter to that self. What did you need to hear then? Can you say these things to yourself now?

What do master narratives have to say about beauty? How do they get it wrong? Write a body narrative that act as a counter-story.

Bodies Transcend:
Dissolving Internalized Boundaries

"There are no shortcuts to wholeness. The only way to become whole is to put our arms lovingly around everything we've shown ourselves to be: self-serving and generous, spiteful and compassionate, cowardly and courageous, treacherous and trustworthy. We must be able to say to ourselves and to the world at large, 'I am all of the above.' "

—PARKER PALMER
On the Brink of Everything

A few months ago, I was uncomfortably tired. I went straight into analysis and fix-it mode. "Why am I so tired? I'm getting enough sleep, I exercise, I eat well. I shouldn't be tired. What's wrong?" One day my friend said to me kindly, "You know, caring for little kids is really tiring, especially while working at home during a pandemic. Maybe that's reason enough." I wanted to dismiss her comment, but I tried it on for size, and it fit. I was making my tiredness bigger than it needed to be by fretting about it and turning it into a problem I needed to solve. I can work and parent well while tired. I can fully enjoy my day while I am tired. Fatigue might be inevitable. The suffering around it is optional. I stopped fretting about my fatigue and just let myself be tired. I let myself feel tired with nothing extra around it. By dropping the story and judgment, the fatigue eased.

I tell myself stories all the time, and some of those stories don't serve me. Some of them perpetuate suffering. Some of those stories limit my own freedom and agency. It's one reason I get on my yoga mat and practice. When I am doing yoga, I place my attention on the task at hand, and the rest falls away. The postures require enough attention that my body gets a much-needed break from the chatty, opinionated roommate in my mind. I drop the story and spend time with myself, letting myself feel what I feel.

Here's a story: I used to believe that my body would depreciate as I aged, getting weaker and less flexible over time. My yoga practice proved that story wrong. I am stronger and more flexible than I have ever been. I put my body in motion, travel to my edge, and dwell there. Now and then, when I'm not trying or striving or clinging, it feels like transcendence. This story-less attention used to happen practicing gymnastics, pitching a softball, and running a marathon. It happens when I write. By choosing tasks that envelope me in my own body, I can unlearn my learned helplessness, interrupt, prove my own limiting stories wrong. I get busy creating and transcend the spiraling.

This section contains prompts about entering your body more fully to dissolve real and perceived boundaries limiting your expansion. You can subvert your own expectations of who you should be to become who you are, remembering your true self and your body's connection to the world. In doing so, you may find balance, rest, and peace.

Mind–body dualism would have us seek transcendence from our bodies by escaping our bodies and existing in the mind. We are learning more and more that we cannot think our way to healing and wholeness. An alternative framing is to turn toward our bodies, drop into our bodies more fully, live in our bodies and in the present moment as home. By becoming more embodied, we get access and connection to what is beyond the body. The only way out is through.

Fill the page with answers. Look at your list and
circle the ones that feel the truest.
"What I really want is..."

Have you ever received a diagnosis that made sense of
symptoms you had? What is your relationship to the label?
Is it limiting? Clarifying? Depressing? Empowering?

Has the presence of your body ever shifted
the energy of a room of people?

Write about a time you realized your body is mortal.

What activities help you more fully inhabit your body? What is your body doing when you experience yourself as pure breath and energy?

What stories are you telling yourself that are limiting?

Who are the coaches, healers, and friends in your life accompanying you to a new level of presence and awareness?

When your body talks to you, what does it say? How does it get your attention?

What is something you loved doing in your body as a child? Have expectations and agreements taken away unencumbered joy in the activity?

Write about the numbers in your life: your GPA, the number of hours you sleep, your blood pressure, your weight, your salary, your age. What stories and limiting beliefs do you attach to those numbers? How could your relationship to your body shift if you revised those stories?

How has your body been labeled by others? How have you labeled your own body? What labels, if any, set you free?

Where do you clench and grip in your body? What do you need to let go of to live into more freedom and agency in your body and life?

What people, places, and activities invite you to rest?
How do you build a sustainable pace for your life?

Wholeness is not perfection. Where in your life do you sense an opportunity to heal toward wholeness?

Have you ever entered so fully into your community that
the boundaries between "you" and "us" dissolved just a bit?
How might your body story help us imagine a world where
interconnection and common good are the air we breathe?

How are we taught to escape our bodies instead of deepening our relationship to them? How might your story join with these to challenge, diversify, and expand our canon?

Write about a time you transcended your body, not by avoiding it, but rather by entering it more fully. This often happens for people while doing things like having sex, playing sports, being in nature, or meditating. What did it feel like to be so in tune with your body that the boundaries between your body and the world faded just a bit?

Which of your body stories might benefit from a revision?

Drop into your body and notice. What do you still need to say? What story in you is ready to be told?

Keep Writing

"The glorification of busy will destroy us. Without space for healing, without time for reflection, without an opportunity to surrender, we risk a complete disconnect from the authentic self...To combat this, we have to form the conscious intention to prioritize our inner life. To notice our breath, our bodies, our feelings. To step back from the fires of overwhelm and remember ourselves. It may feel counterintuitive in a culture that is speed addicted, but the slower we can become, the quicker we can return home."

—JEFF BROWN
Hearticulations

On a Sunday morning in early October, I bike to the lake close to my house to watch throngs of runners participate in the Twin Cities Marathon. Waves and waves of runners with different body shapes, sizes, and ages pass by. Some are smiling, proud and playful. Others are struggling already. I've missed the leaders, running with ease and speed. These are the runners who run just to run, who run to finish.

T-shirts tell stories. One runner is running her 100th marathon. Another is running on his sixth continent. One runner is juggling and yet another is running backward. I see knock-knees, wheelchairs, and rainbow tutus. Perfectly imperfect bodies running. Each runner has a different backstory. One runner is running in memory of her mother, another to raise awareness about diabetes. For some the training was easy and this will be just another day jogging. For others, it is the pinnacle of a long and arduous road filled with self-doubt and struggle. The stories come together and meet in this moment on the journey, sharing the path for a few hours. The density and compression of their stories, converging and melding together into one collective event, carries a palpable weight. Each runner takes a risk in showing up, in their commitment, in their forethought. They risk by running in public, in community. They do not need their free shirt and participant medal to know they belong to this hodgepodge makeshift community of bodies.

I stand on the sidelines with the other spectators, bundled up and holding coffee, toting cow bells and signs, witnessing and watching, enamored, impressed, and inspired. I cry a little at the beauty of it all and cannot help but cheer them on. Part of me desperately wants to jump in with them and run.

In working through this journal, I hope you join me in seeing the beauty of it all. I hope you jump in with me and run. Our bodies—all our bodies—are messy, beautiful, imperfect, and revelatory. It's what makes us human. Stories cannot contain them, but they can create space for our sense of identity to expand. Keep writing. Pick up a pen again and again. Use the prompts. Set a timer. Don't overthink it. Write for you. Write to get deeper into your body and work through the stuck energy living there. You do not need to be a trained writer to understand the contours of your memories and comprehend what your body has endured. You can live into narrative repair. You can write your body narrative to bring healing and wholeness. You can unfold toward a sense of renewal, restored to your remarkable and beautiful body. We can write our body stories to honor and remember. And in doing so, our stories can also witness and create a vision. bell hooks writes, "The function of art is to do more than tell it like it is—it's to imagine what is possible." We can write and share our body narratives in a way that casts us in a role of wholeness and in a way that shifts our master narratives. We can know more freedom and agency and help work toward that for others. We can live into a new society that values the wisdom of bodies and approaches all bodies with curiosity and reverence.

Visibility is not the same as belonging. If and when it feels safe, share your body stories knowing that visibility matters and hoping that we can all grow our capacity to listen to each other's body stories and work toward legislation that protects and advocates for all bodies. We all have a desire to belong, and it is our collective work to build new, more beautiful things to belong to as well as new ways of belonging. I believe our children are growing up in a more expansive narrative landscape that makes room for more body diversity with more visible paths forward. May our stories be the beginning—not the end—of our work for more belonging.

My hope for you is that choosing the embodied path deepens your sense of feeling seen. I hope it brings healing and wholeness. I hope you find home in your body, a place you do not have the urge to escape from. And I hope that what emerges from our work to inhabit our bodies more fully is a more beautiful, varied and thriving community of which to belong.

*Fill in 2-9 with moments on the journey that seem like life posts
Then pick 2 points next to each other and tell a story
that connect them. Write the in-between.*

1. I was born....

2.

3.

4.

5.

6.

7.

8.

9.

10. Right now...

It's really important for me not to be perceived as _____.

Write about a meal that you left feeling totally nourished. What were you eating? Who were you with? What were you talking about?

What are activities, who are people, what are foods that nourish you? Are you prioritizing your own nourishment?

Write a permission slip for yourself. What do you
need to grant yourself permission for today?

Pádraig Ó Tuama wrote, "You are the place where I stand on the day
when my feet are sore." Who is the "you" in that phrase for you?

Spend three minutes writing about something that brings up shame. Naming it can often dispel the shame, even just a bit.

I am no longer waiting for...

Where in your life or work are you pursuing comfort
when what is called for is discomfort?

Intentionally enter a space where you are not an insider. Simply notice what happens to your body and how you feel. Go home and write down some observations about the experience.

Write about how you are unlearning things that don't serve your body.

Write down a fear that is taking up space. Ask, "What then?" Let that fear play out. What if that fear came true? Keep asking, "What then?" And play it our until the fear becomes more manageable.

Write about a time you broke a bone, a promise, a law, or a heart.

Choose a random age and write a self-portrait of yourself at that age.

In what ways have you yet to accept the fact that you are the person you are and not the person you think you ought to be?

What are you grieving? What are you grateful for?

Write about a time you were literally or figuratively lost.
What do you know now that you didn't know then?

For a few minutes, write about what you hope for in the coming days, weeks, and months. Then from what comes up create a one-word mantra you can take on and circle back to. Be hope in action. Create it.

These are the kind of things we need for the tired spaces of our world. This is the way we need to move forward in a world that is so interested in being comforted by the damp blanket of bad stories. We need stories of belonging that move us towards each other, not from each other; ways of being human that open up the possibilities of being alive together; ways of navigating our differences that deepen our curiosity, that deepen our friendship, that deepen our capacity to disagree, that deepen the argument of being alive. This is what we need. This is what will save us. This is the work of peace. This is the work of imagination.

—PÁDRAIG Ó TUAMA
ON BEING

Recommended Resources

Still Writing by Dani Shapiro

Several Short Sentences on Writing by Verlyn Klinkenborg

Writing Down the Bones by Natalie Gorman

Body Work by Melissa Febos

Remembered Rapture: The Writer at Work by bell hooks

On Writing by Stephen King

Pelvic Liberation by Leslie Howard

My Grandmother's Hands: Racialized Trauma and the Pathway to Mending Our Hearts and Bodies by Resmaa Menakem

Burnout: The Secret to Unlocking the Stress Cycle by Emily Nagoski and Amelia Nagoski

Damaged Identity, Narrative Repair by Hilde Lindemann Nelson

The Body Keeps the Score: Brain, Mind, and Body in the Healing of Trauma by Bessel van der Kolk, MD

The Clarity Cleanse: 12 Steps to Finding Renewed Energy, Spiritual Fulfillment, and Emotional Healing by Dr. Habib Sadeghi